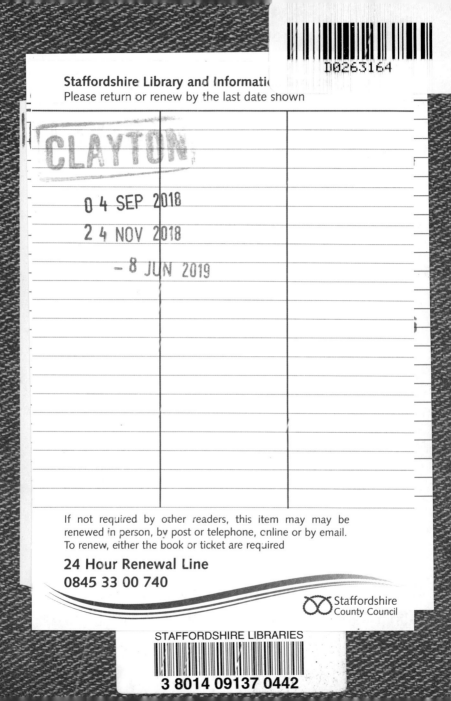

For Molly, who (just like
Tigger) is always fun, fun,
fun, fun, FUN!!
KMcC

First published 2010 by Walker Books Ltd
87 Vauxhall Walker, London SE11 5HJ

2 4 6 8 10 9 7 5 3 1

Text © 2010 Karen McCombie
Illustrations © 2010 Lydia Monks

The right of Karen McCombie and Lydia Monks to be identified as author and
illustrator respectively of this work has been asserted by them in accordance
with the Copyright, Designs and Patents Act 1988

This book has been typeset in Granjon

Printed and bound in Great Britain by
J F Print Ltd., Sparkford

British Library Cataloguing in Publication Data
is available from the British Library.
ISBN 978-1-4063-1191-4

www.walker.co.uk

KAREN McCOMBIE · LYDIA MONKS

Indie Kidd's (Most Excellent) Guide to

Fun for Free

WALKER
BOOKS

Indie Kidd's (Most Excellent) Guide to Fun for Free

CONTENTS

47 Fun with more than one

One is good but two is better (specially when the other person is Mum).

57 More ways to have fun with more than one

Tennis, football and food (but not how you expect them to be!).

67 Fun with friends

Soph, Fee, Dylan and me – and the sleepover with a difference.

77 More ways to have fun with friends

Involving bad-acting, bin-bags and plenty of hip-wiggling.

…and when fun stuff goes wrong!

How to have fun!

(Specially when you're not expecting any...)

A gorgeous, delicious, fun-filled week off school was coming up, but I felt **blaaaaaaahhhhh**...

Miss Levy, my teacher, didn't seem to notice.

"Right, everyone! It's nearly bell-time, so let's spend the last few minutes talking about our plans for the holidays!" she said brightly.

It was alright for Miss Levy to sound bright; she'd already told us that she was going to Florida to swim with dolphins.

"Sophie? What are you up to?" Miss Levy smiled at Soph, one of my best(est) friends.

"I'm going to visit my cousins in Paris, and then we're going to Disneyland!!" said Soph.

"Fantastic! And what about you, Sophie?" Miss Levy smiled at Fee, my other best(est) friend.

"We're going to Centreparcs in Suffolk! I'm going to cycle and swim and go horseriding!" said Fee.

Heaps more people had their hands up, and heaps more people spoke about the fun stuff they were going to do.

Some were going on holiday.

Some were visiting friends or relatives.

Some had friends or relatives coming to visit them.

Some were going to the school's holiday club, where they got to play games and make stuff and go on trips while their parents were working.

Some – OK, just Simon Green – said he was going to play his big brother's zombie-zapping Wii game every day.

I wished I … well, I wished I was doing any of that stuff (except the zombie-zapping Wii game).

"Indie? What are your plans?"

Miss Levy was still smiling, not realising just how **blaaaahhh** I felt, and probably expecting me to say something fun.

But what was going to be fun about my holiday?

It was going to be a fun-free zone, for sure.

Here's why:

• My two best(est) friends would be in France and Suffolk.

• My mum (who is the manager of an animal rescue centre) was on a training course for most of the time.

• My dad (who is my dad) was going to some place I couldn't remember the name of with Fiona (who is my step-mum) and Dylan (who is my step-brother) to visit Dylan's grandparents.

• Caitlin, who is nineteen and our lodger and my childminder and mad (in a nice way) was going to be looking after me. Normally, this would be excellent, but there was a problem...

"Well? Doing anything nice, Indie?" Miss Levy asked again.

"No," I answered in a flat-as-a-pancake voice.

"Oh!" said Miss Levy, maybe spotting my **blaaaahhhh-ness** at last. "Why's that?"

"My childminder is on crutches," I mumbled some more, "so we can't do anything fun."

"Oh, dear. What happened to her?" asked Miss Levy.

"She tore a liga…thing."

Simon Green started sniggering, as if I'd said something rude. You can say dumb stuff like 'pomegranate' or 'ladle' and Simon Green will snigger like it's a rude word.

"A ligament?" Miss Levy said to me, while throwing a sharp look at Simon Green. "Well, that must be very pain–"

BRIIINNNGGGG!!!!

The bell went and twenty-nine holiday hungry kids started scrambling for their schoolbags.

"–ful!" Miss Levy finished. "Now of course, there will be HOLIDAY HOMEWORK!!"

Everyone groaned.

"I want a project from everyone about your holiday best bits!!"

Everyone cheered (since it wasn't something complicated like seventy-five questions about fractions or writing a report on the local water treatment plant.)

Pleased to see everyone looking so pleased, Miss Levy clapped her hands together, which was her signal that everyone could go.

Except me.

"Can you stay behind for a second, Indie?" Miss Levy mouthed at me, as kids zoomed out of the class.

17

I grabbed my bag and slouched over to Miss Levy's desk.

"So, Indie ... how about we figure out a way for you to have a good time this holiday?" she said, once the door had banged shut and we weren't so deafened by Simon Green making rat-a-tat shooting noises down the corridor (practising zapping zombies already, I guess).

I looked at Miss Levy hopefully.

WOW – was she going to invite me along on her dolphin-spotting trip to Florida?

"You have a fantastic imagination, Indie, and you're great at doing projects," Miss Levy continued. "So here's what I was thinking ... why don't you put together a project about how to have fun, in the simplest of ways?"

To be honest, I'd rather have hung out with dolphins for a week, but I guess teachers don't generally invite their pupils to come on holiday with them.

So, the idea of doing a project on fun... Well, if I forgot about the dolphins, I guess it did sound sort of **fun**.

All of a sudden, a bunch of **fun-ish** stuff sprung into my mind.

I remembered giggling my way around the obstacle course made out of sofa cushions with Dad and Dylan a while back.

And then there was the time I dressed up Dibbles and sent his photo to the local newspaper competition. And what about when I played 'What's The Time, Mr Vampire' with all the small kids at school? (Caitlin invented that!)

Those three things were **fun** and **simple** (and didn't cost much or anything at all, which is always good). And it had only taken me about five seconds to think of them.

If I spent a whole week thinking of more stuff like that I was pretty sure I could write a project Miss Levy would be proud of.

"I could call it

Indie Kidd's (MOST Excellent) Doing-Fun-Things-That-Are-Simple-And-Don't-cost-Much-Money Project'!!"

I said excitedly, as my head began pinging full of ideas.

"Um, yes ... that's, er, catchy," said Miss Levy, with a bit of a wibbly smile on her face. (I think it's 'cause she felt so proud of me.)

Then she said that maybe at the start of next term she'd help me make my project into a booklet. She said it could be handed out to everyone in class, so that they'd always have ideas of fun stuff to do too. **Yay!**

And now, well, it's one week later, and **ta-DAH!**, I have done my whole project, with a bit of help (well, quite a lot of help) from Caitlin* (from the comfort of the sofa).

I remembered and wrote down stories of brilliant (and brilliantly dumb) fun stuff I've done on my own or with my friends and family.

And Caitlin came up with some very **cool** (and sometimes slightly *weird*) ways to entertain yourself as well.

Right, I'm off to do a family tree for my goldfish (yes, it's as nuts as it sounds, see page 142).

Love,
Indie Kidd xxx

* Wait a minute; maybe that means I'll have to call it

'Indie Kidd and Caitlin's (Most Excellent) Doing-Fun-Things-That-Are-Simple-And-Don't-cost-Much-Money Project'.

(OK, I might have to work on that title…)

Fun for one

(How I invented nicely mysterious surprises...)

"Bye, honey!" said Mum on Monday morning, stroking me on the top of the head, till she remembered I wasn't one of the dogs, and gave me a kiss instead.

We were on the doorstep. Mum was blinking, trying to remember things she might have forgotten. Like her lunch.

24

"Bye, Mum!" I said, handing her a peanut butter sandwich to take with her, on her how-to-help-rescue-animals course.

"Oh, thank you, Indie! You are so thoughtful!" she gushed, giving me such a tight hug that the mobile in her top pocket got squished and accidentally dialled Caitlin's number.

("Hello? Hello?" I heard Caitlin saying through in the kitchen.)

Mum's tight hug: it wasn't just for the peanut butter sandwich, I knew. It was 'cause she still felt **bad** about having to be on a course this week. Dad was feeling **guilty** too. When I'd gone round on Sunday afternoon, he gave me three times my normal pocket money and told me a hundred times that I could phone him whenever I wanted to while he, Fiona and Dylan were away in … wherever it was they were going.

My stepmum Fiona – who is the cooking editor of the local newspaper – was feeling **guilty** as well. I knew that for sure 'cause she gave me a whole homemade raspberry and vanilla cheesecake to take back here with me.

"You'll be fine with Caitlin, though, won't you, Indie?" Mum asked me hopefully.

Over her shoulder I saw Mrs O'Neill from across the road, out dusting her hedge. She always does that in the morning – she gets a bit lonely and it's her way of having a conversation with passing neighbours.

"Of course!" I nodded, as I waved to Mrs O'Neill. She waved her duster back. "We're going to start my project on fun today!"

"Yes! Well, have, er, fun!" Mum called out, as she walked over to her van, and tried to open it by pointing and pressing on her peanut butter sandwich, instead of the key fob she was holding in her other hand.

OK, from one *ditzy* grown-up to another...

"Hello? Hello? Is anyone there?" Caitlin was still saying into her phone as I walked into the kitchen.

She shook her head and clicked the red button.

"**Hey, kid!**" she semi-yawned in my direction. "I just got together some stuff you'll need for your project!"

And the everything laid out on the kitchen table was…

- paper (a big pile)
- pens (glitter gel ones)
- cheesecake (minus the three slices me, Mum and Caitlin had had for pudding last night)

"**Great!!**" I said, pulling out a chair.

Then I noticed that Caitlin was yawning again.

"Are you alright?" I asked.

"Mmm," she mumbled drowsily. "I couldn't sleep last night – I kept rolling on to my sore leg and waking myself up."

"Well, why don't you go and have a nap?" I suggested. "I can start this on my own."

"Yeah?" Caitlin yawned gratefully. "OK, just half-an-hour, kid."

An hour-and-a-quarter later, I was still alone (with Dibbles' head flopped in my lap, drooling).

On the pages and pages of white paper in front of me there were precisely no ace **fun-for-free** ideas.

Instead, there were just oodles and oodles of doodles. Doodles of stars, hearts, flowers and – most of all – smiley faces.

I didn't know why I'd drawn the smileys. I mean, since I hadn't come up with one fun idea so far, I was feeling a weeny bit gloomy.

(Maybe I should have drawn frownies instead.)

But the smileys seemed to be smiling up at me.

It made me think of poor, tired Caitlin, with her painful, torn liga-thingy. She'd probably much prefer a week of sofa-lounging, watching day-time telly, than trying to entertain a ten-year-old girl (me).

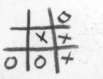

Suddenly, I wanted to do something nice for Caitlin.

So I drew a big smiley in extra-thick gel pen (purply-pink).

And another one.

And another one.

And eight more identical smiley faces, only with one small difference; all the smiles on their smiley faces got

bigger,
 and
  bigger
  and
   BIGGER

each time.

Next, I cut around them in small, same-sized squares, stapled all the squares together, and **TA NA!!!** I had invented a smiley flicker-book!

Tiptoeing through to Caitlin's room, I left her gift — shhhhhh! — on her pillow as she snoozed.

I reckoned it would just be a **cute, happy** thing to wake up to (and flick through).

Then I thought of another someone who might appreciate a **cute, happy** something.

Someone who liked dusting things that didn't need dusting.

Quickly – while I felt all inspired – I drew an orange glitter pen smiley, and this time added a poem under it. It read:

Well, hello, Mrs O'Neill,
Just thought I'd write and say
That you've extremely
       nice to know
And I wish you a Very Happy Day!

I didn't say who it was from, just so it would be a nicely mysterious surprise popping through our lonely old lady neighbour's letterbox.

After that, I went smiley crazy, drawing three more smileys, with Welcome Home!! messages beside them.

Soph's was a smiley with Mickey Mouse's ears added on, in honour of her trip to Disneyland Paris.

Fee's smiley was on the front of an envelope that had a hand-drawn (by me) map inside it, which went from Centreparcs to here with 'YAY! YOU'RE HOME!' scribbled beside my doodle of her house.

Dylan's smiley was on a serviette inside a sandwich bag. Underneath it, I'd written,

Missed you.

Come tell me about your holiday. Bring biscuits (home-made by your mum, please) Love, Guess who? x

I figured that maybe Mum could drop them off at my various friends' houses on her way to the course this week. That way the smileys could be waiting for Soph, Fee and Dylan once they got back from

France, Suffolk and wherever-it-was that Dylan was going.

"Hey, kid!" said a sleepy-but-more-human Caitlin twenty minutes later. "What's this **cute** little thing?"

She was flicking through her flicker-book, her smile growing at the same time as her smiley's grin grew.

"That," I told her, proudly, "is my FIRST fun-for-free project idea."

And it was too.

Caitlin suggested that we staple her smiley flicker-book into this project, since it was practically a historic document.

It's just a pity Dibbles ate it while me and Caitlin got stuck into the cheesecake.

MORE WAYS TO HAVE FUN FOR FREE WHEN YOU'RE ONE (ER, PERSON)

Do a project

It doesn't have to be a **fun-for-free** project like mine. It could be a how-fit-can-I-get-in-a-week? project, or an I-CAN-manage-not-to-be-narky-with-my-family-for-a-whole-week! project.

Re-style your room

Caitlin asked me how long my room had looked the way it had. When she said that, I realised that apart from a couple of posters, it looked just about the same as it had when I was little.

"Probably ten years," I told her.

"And you're how old?" she asked, knowing that I was – yeah – ten.

And so while Caitlin stood in the doorway and said encouraging things, I shuffled some furniture around. (Not the wardrobe – I didn't want to die from it falling on top of me.)

After that, I put different stuff on different shelves and different pictures on different hooks.

Then looking around, I realised I had a whole new(ish) room. **Excellent!**

(Though Smudge did get confused when she tried to jump on the bed for a snooze and found herself in my wicker waste-paper basket.)

Write a These Are A Few Of My Favourite Things* list, and hide it away for a year.

Caitlin did this when she was twelve. When she looked at it aged thirteen, she couldn't believe what incredible bad taste she had in friends, crushes, bands and food (she'd had a craze for marshmallow sandwiches at the time).

I have decided I will try this. (Writing a These Are A Few Of My Favourite Things list AND marshmallow sandwiches, I mean…)

(*This is the name of a song from a famous old film called 'The Sound Of Music'. Caitlin says it's great and we'll get it out on DVD sometime to watch together. She says it's a musical about nuns and Nazis, which doesn't sound too cheerful. I may need several marshmallow sandwiches to see me through it.)

Pamper your pets

Everyone can get a bit used to their pets, and sort of see them like part of the furniture (part of the furniture that sheds hair and poos…).

So whether you've got a Great Dane or a goldfish, maybe spend some quality time with them, grooming them (not if they're a goldfish), stroking them (not if they're a goldfish either) or letting them out for a run (definitely not for a goldfish).

Think of making your pet's home more comfy or interesting, like getting a chunk of wood from the park for your hamster to scramble over.

Or do like I did and paint an interesting scene on a piece of cardboard and wrap it round the fish tank. (I did the skyline of New York, and added the London Eye for interest.)

If you don't have a pet to pamper, then think of ways to pamper your granny, or someone.

(Note: grans like hugs and cups of tea more than sticks from the park and being groomed.)

Invent a mantra

Another of Caitlin's ideas. She's said that when she was about fifteen, a bunch of girls started teasing her about her hair (she had a blue fringe, apparently).

And how she accessorised her school uniform (day-glo pink tights and matching nail varnish).

And the sort of music she liked (old punk stuff that her dad got her into).

They called her a blue-haired, pink punk weirdo, which I guess was strictly true, but sounds mean when you say it that way.

She got quite down about it, till she invented a mantra – a word or saying you repeat to yourself – that she did every day before she left for school.

She'd look in mirror as she brushed her blue fringe, and say **"I'm a NICE person! I'm a NICE person! I'm a NICE person!"** a bunch of times.

If anyone started saying mean stuff at school, she'd just block out their burbling and listen to the mantra she was saying in her head instead.

But anyone can invent a mantra about anything to do with themselves.

I was going to do "**I must NOT eat five pieces of cheesecake in a row because it makes me feel sick**" but Caitlin said it has to be a positive mantra. (Though I sort of think that reminding myself not to do something that makes me feel sick is pretty positive.)

She says it should be something like "I am IMPORTANT!" (if you generally get the feeling you aren't) or "I am good at LOTS of stuff!" (if you feel there's other stuff you aren't good at).

I haven't got a mantra yet. I will work on having one by the end of this project.

(Hey, how about "I WILL have a mantra by the end of this project"?)

Fun with more than one

(The time Mum gave me a score of 4.5 for my skill in socks...)

Chickenpox is very annoying.

Dylan says it's annoying because it's got 'chicken' in the name but has nothing to do with chickens. (Dylan says chickens should be very annoyed as it gives them a bad reputation.)

But back when I was eight years old, the reason I found chickenpox annoying was that the doctor orders you to stay off school for a whole, dull week when you have it, even though you feel spotty but fine.

"Finished reading your book?" Mum asked, on the fifth day of me being stuck indoors.

I'd slobbed on through to the kitchen, to find Mum pulling all her work clothes out of the tumble-dryer.

Thudding my book down on the table, I thudded myself down on a chair too.

"Yes, I've finished," I said flatly.

"So, are you going to start reading another one?" Mum asked cheerfully, looking at me over the top of a teetering pile of laundry.

"Not really in the mood," I answered her flatly.

In the last five days I had...

- read lots of books
- done lots of drawing
- watched lots of TV
- tidied loads of drawers and cupboards and dark corners in my room
- stared very hard for a very long time at the goldfish swimming round and round (and round) their tank.

(Back then, they were called
William and Harry, and those were
the goldfish that came before One,
Two, Three, Four, Five, Five-and-
a-half and Brian the Angelfish.)
  • played lots of doggy-tug-
    of-war with George and
      Kenneth (once at the
       same time; they won,
      surprise, surprise)
     • stroked Smudge so much
I was in danger of
wearing a bald
patch in her fur.

Mum (on leave
from the Rescue Centre
to look after me) was running out of things
to cheer me up with.

I think she was running out of ways to cheer herself up too.

Mum's head is always so madly into caring for animals that she's never been very good at housework. But because she'd been stuck at home with me all that week, she'd done a whole heap of housework, and none of it very well.

"Maybe we could go out for a walk?" she suggested.

Though Mum was looking warily at my very spotty face when she spoke.

Even though I really wanted some fresh air and exercise, I was worried that my face would frighten small children and nervous animals.

"The floor!" Mum suddenly yelped. "It's slippy!"

"Yeah ... I know – I have to be careful

on it. You already told me," I muttered, frowning at her. She'd used the wrong type of cleaner on it and Kenneth had done the splits on it earlier.

"Here!" Mum said next, chucking me a pair of her thick, woolly work socks from the top of the laundry pile.

"What am I meant to do with them?" I asked, catching them in my hands.

Had she gone mad? As crazy as me, after being stuck in the house for so long?

"Put them on!" she laughed, at the same time as she...

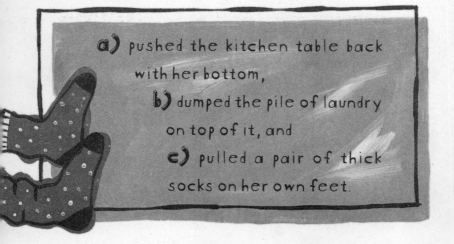

a) pushed the kitchen table back with her bottom,

b) dumped the pile of laundry on top of it, and

c) pulled a pair of thick socks on her own feet.

I did what I was told ('cause that's what eight-year-old kids are meant to do), and stared at her, wondering what was coming next.

"'Dancing On Ice'!!" she said.

"It's, er, not on right now..." I replied, wondering what she was talking about. OK, I guessed that she was talking about that celebrities' ice-skating competition, but it hadn't been on telly in ages. And what did that have to do with woolly socks and...

"Let's skate!" she announced, holding out her arms to me.

...slippy floors?!

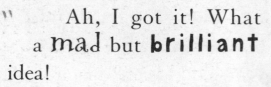

"Ah, I got it! What a **mad** but **brilliant** idea!

Me and Mum clasped hands and set off.

We zoomed (as far as the fridge).

We twirled (she banged her foot on the bin).

We struck poses (I've never felt so elegant in ugly socks).

Mum even tried to give me a lift (quite good fun for me, but something went ping in her back).

While Mum sat down for a breather, I did some pretty graceful jumps (just missing Kenneth's head by a millimetre).

I had been concentrating so hard that I hadn't noticed her scribbling. When I

stopped and took a bow, she held up an electricity bill with '4.5' written on it in marker pen.

"For technical merit," said Mum, with a very straight face.

I've done lots of sock-skating since, with Soph and Fee and Dylan, and even though Mum learned her lesson and the floor has never been polished in such a deadly way again, it's still always fun.

Though I've never got such a high score as I did that time with Mum.

(Mainly 'cause I've usually been sniggering too much to sock-skate to the best of my technical ability…)

MORE WAYS TO HAVE FUN FOR FREE WITH MORE THAN ONE

Air football

Me and Dylan did this one time at his house. Here's how:

1. Find a kitchen floor (available in every home).

2. Make goals from plastic tubs turned on their sides (available in kitchen cupboards), and Blu-tack or Sellotape them to the kitchen floor.

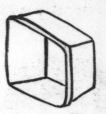

3. Grab some empty toilet roll holders (available in every bathroom*), cut them down one side, then curl tighter and tape them back up so the cylinder is a weeny bit narrower, and you have a perfect 'blower'.

4. Squish a ball out of a crushed up sheet of paper (available somewhere in the house).

5. Get down on your knees and try to 'blow' a goal!

* I hadn't realised that there were no empty toilet roll holders around at the time Dylan came up with this idea. I only found out when Fiona threw a fit at finding a floppy mountain of unravelled toilet paper piled on top of the cistern. (Seriously not good for someone with an allergy to messiness, like my step-mum.)

Paper plate tennis

When you've finished your game of air football, rescue the 'ball' and...

1. Get two paper plates
2. Play tennis instead!

Have a stupid food cook-off

Make something nice to eat for a friend or relative, only make it dumb-looking. Excellent examples:

- Soph's under-the-sea jelly (green, with plastic goldfish and a mermaid dropped in while it was setting)

- Dad's chip fort: made out of, er, upright chips, cut into various heights, stuck together with mayonnaise.

• Fiona's Mount Vesuvius muffins (muffin with red lava icing, served with a sparkler). My step-mum might not be very good with silliness, but she makes an exception when it comes to food!

The Who-Am-I? game

This is a version of the game where you give another player an identity, and they have to guess who they are by asking stuff like "Am I famous?".

61

Me and Caitlin have come up with a more interesting version: an animal one. Do a list of questions the guesser can ask, like "Am I slimy?", "Am I icky?", "Would I like to eat you?" and "Would you want to cuddle me?" (Only include the funniest questions. Sensible questions like "Am I nocturnal?" are not allowed.)

Make a memoir

On the Thursday of my holiday, Mum came home from her course at lunchtime to ferry Caitlin to the hospital for a check up on how her liga-thingy was mending.

I had two options: go with them and hang out at the non-interesting hospital, or hang out with Mrs O'Neill across the road.

I chose hanging out with Mrs O'Neill, 'cause I thought it would be nice to keep her company (even though she talks about the price of jam a lot) AND 'cause I could maybe play with her budgie, Archie.

But when I went over, Archie was in trouble. Mrs O'Neill had got him from the Rescue Centre, and his old owner had taught him to say a few words, like "Hello!" and "Ooooh, nice!" Mrs O'Neill thought that was all, except he'd just that minute come out with a **Very Rude Word** (eek!).

Because there's no naughty step for budgies, she'd put a bath-towel over his over his cage instead.

Hmmm. That meant I'd have to listen to Mrs O'Neill chattering about jam and dusting. **Double hmmm.**

Still, while she went to fetch me a juice, I looked at all the old black and white photos dotted around her living room. It reminded me a bit of those programmes on telly where they trace the ancestors of a famous person. **Aha**...

Mrs O'Neill wasn't famous, but I bet she had lots of interesting stories to tell about her life, and growing up in the 1800s. (I wasn't really sure how old she was exactly.)

As she came back into the room, I was scrabbling about for the notebook I knew I had in my bag (free with the magazine I bought on Saturday).

"Can I interview you?" I asked her.

Mrs O'Neill looked as surprised as if I'd asked her to do the can-can for me.

But we had a lovely time. She told me (too fast) all about her childhood, about her her favourite toys and her friends and her family (her granny ran a grocer's shop, so she probably inherited her interest in the price of jam there).

I have promised Mrs O'Neill that I will turn my notes into a memoir (Caitlin said that's a posh, French way of saying 'life story').

I hope Mrs O'Neill will like it and not mind that I have missed out bits because she spoke too fast and I wrote too slow.

Actually, if you fancy being a journalist and want to interview someone, see if you can borrow something to record them with. That way you won't have to ask them to speak in slooowwwww motioooonnnnn…

Fun with friends

(Soph, Fee, Dylan and me – and the sleepover with a difference!)

Last Saturday morning I woke up to Dibbles snoring, my arm prickling with pins and needles ('cause Dibbles was sleeping on it) and pouring rain.

The rain part was **majorly bad.**

That's 'cause me, Soph and Fee had been planning to have a picnic in the park that afternoon.

We'd got it all sorted; we were all going to bring different kinds of food each. Soph was in charge of starters (crisps), I was doing main course (Scotch eggs from the supermarket) and Fee was going to bring salad (some carrots).

Dylan was coming too, which was **brilliant**, because the night before he'd texted me to say his mum Fiona had just invented raspberry yogurt and raisin cookies, and that sounded very good for pudding.

"Oh, Indie, honey, what's wrong?" asked Mum, when I wandered into the kitchen five minutes after spotting the picnic-unfriendly rain.

She was hand-feeding a baby rabbit that she'd brought home from the Rescue Centre. It blinked and looked all worried when it saw me, laying its ears flat against the side of its head.

Mum did the same (only without the floppy ears).

I think if you got my face translated it would have said, "Alas! A terrible, terrible disaster has occurred!!"

"It's raining!" I moaned.

Mum relaxed a bit. I guess a bit of rain didn't sound too much of a disaster.

"Is it?" she asked vaguely, turning round as if she was trying to locate a window.

"Me and Soph and Fee were supposed to have a picnic today!" I reminded my *ditzy* mum. "We have all the food! Even Dylan's coming with biscuits!!"

"Um, well maybe the rain will go off?" Mum suggested hopefully.

We both looked at the kitchen window, which was being lashed by torrential rain. It was as if someone was standing outside chucking buckets of water at the glass.

"I might as well stay in my pyjamas all day…" I said glumly, alarming the baby rabbit again with my bad case of gloom.

And so I trudged back to my room and slunk under the duvet, wondering which of my friends I'd call first to moan about the picnic we weren't going to have.

Ping!

From nowhere,
a teeny-tiny idea crept
into my head.

It was to do with
my pyjamas…

Suddenly, I scrambled out
of bed and hurtled downstairs.

"I've got a new plan!" I yelled at Mum.
"We can have a sleepover INSTEAD!!"

Mum looked startled and slightly confused. The baby rabbit looked very frightened.

"A daytime sleepover!" I whispered my explanation. "I'll ask everyone to come here and bring their duvets and pyjamas!"

Three hours later, the floor of my room looked like one big, patchwork duvet.

I was in my spottiest flannelette pyjamas; Soph came in her High School Musical long nightie; Fee wore a flowery purple top and leggings, and Dylan was in his Bob the Builder PJs (no, I didn't realize they made those for nine-year-olds either).

"So what do we do?" Soph asked excitedly.

"Close the curtains and pretend it's night-time, of course!" I told her.

And so we pulled the curtains.

"What now?" asked Fee with a frown, since she wasn't sure what this daytime sleepover involved exactly.

Because Fee's a bit of a worrier, I didn't tell her that I wasn't sure either, and that I was just making it up as I went along.

"Um…" I muttered, glancing around and then spying my CD player. "We have a DISCO, of course!!"

Two seconds later, Fee wasn't frowning – she was **dancing** and **whooping** just as madly as the rest of us as we **bounced** around the room in our jim-jams. (Dylan flicked the light on and off for a dazzling disco effect.)

"What now?" panted Soph, six very fast tracks later.

"It's time for a midnight feast!" I decided on the spot, looking down at my friends flopped on the duvet-splattered floor.

And so we had a midnight feast (our picnic crisps, carrots, Scotch eggs and cookies) at quarter to three in the afternoon.

"Can we come in?" Mum's voice called from the other side of the door a while later, as we squabbled over the last cookie.

But the squabble was soon forgotten, as she stepped into my room with the baby rabbit, and we all cooed very softly over it.

Fee didn't coo quite so much when she realised half-an-hour later that it had pooed in one of her High School Musical slippers.

She might normally have laughed about it, but I think her nerves were jangling by then, since we'd put my bedside light off and started telling ghost stories. (Dibbles helped the atmosphere by doing a yodelly howl along with Dylan's rubbish werewolf story.)

"Wow – that was the best non-picnic I have ever had been to!!" announced Soph, with a happy sigh at five o'clock, when her mum came to collect her.

Me and my friends are planning lots more daytime sleepovers now, and have decided they are **WAY** better than night-time sleepovers, since you have to actually sleep during those, which is a waste of valuble dancing/eating/story-telling hours if you ask me…

MORE WAYS TO HAVE FUN FOR FREE WITH FRIENDS

Mad mini theatre

Cut a up a small cardboard box to make your stage ("Like a dishwasher tablet box," suggests Caitlin). Draw faces and hair onto your fingertips, and act out stuff from school with your 'finger' puppets.

Or do a tiny, dopey version of 'X Factor'. (Caitlin taped half a straw on to her pinkie. It was supposed to look like a tiddly didgeridoo. Sort of.)

Anti-fashion show

One person is the commentator, and everyone else is a model. Models must...

1. Design their own outfits (from random stuff found around the house)

2. Be imaginative (jumpers worn as trousers, clothes pegs earrings etc)

3. Not laugh as they sashay up and down the hall to very funky music in very terrible clothes

(A round of applause for Dylan, who modelled my swimsuit and Mum's wellies, accessorised with oven gloves.)

Act out a film you love

Only it's a five-minute version.

Write a weeny script, get all your props, rehearse it, and perform your mini-masterpiece for your friends or family.

Give a point to anyone who can actually guess what the film's supposed to be from your performance.

(Suggestion: don't pick 'Wal-E' to do. Because it's silent except for a few squeaks, it's hard to guess. Mum didn't get it at all when me and Caitlin performed it, though the squeaking did make Kenneth start to howl.)

79

Trick photography

Once, me, Soph and Fee borrowed Fee's mum's digital camera. Then we tied Fee's favourite cute 'n' dumb old soft toy from the washing line by a piece of string.

Next, Fee got me and Soph to stand way, way back from the washing line and look frightened. (She shouted to us where we needed to be exactly.)

Then **snap!** – she took a photo.

In it, me and Fee looked as if we were just about to be eaten by a large, frightening, carnivorous teddy. **Excellent!**

Surprise makeover

Get some eye shadow and lip gloss out and be a make-up artist to your friends.

The surprise is, you do it with a blindfold.

(Warning: do not go out in public afterwards without using face wipes first. Soph did, and got laughed and pointed at so much she had to dive into the loos in the bus station for an emergency face wash.)

Devise a personality quiz

Everyone should come up with mad questions, like "If you were a vegetable, what would you be?", "What would you rather have: scales or a trunk?", and "If your nose had to be a colour, which would you pick?").

Everyone should then write down their answers and read them out, one by one.

(It was very interesting to know that I was a red-nosed, scaly carrot.)

Rubbish superheroes to the rescue!

Set a challenge to invent rubbish superhero costumes using only stuff you find around the house. Give yourselves a rubbish superhero name and powers.

When we did it, poor Dibbles became Bat-dog, thanks to a bin-bag cape and a badly made mask.

Mr Lumionous (Dylan wrapped in tin-foil, with a torch) decided that Dibbles' superpower should be having the ability to sniff food from three rooms away.

I argued that this can't be a super-power, as he does that anyway.

Old-fashioned fun

(i.e. what your parents did when they were kids)

Travel way, way, way back in time, to last Christmas. Or the Sunday just after it, when I was round at Dad and Fiona's.

84

"Dylan, darling, do you have to be glued to that thing all the time?" asked my stepmother Fiona, staring down at Dylan, as his thumbs jiggled about over the controls of his new DS Lite.

"You and Mike did buy this, Mum!" he pointed out to her, without looking up.

"Yes, but the thing is, Dylan," said my dad gently, "Indie is only here for the afternoon, so we should do something fun together!!"

"Like what?" I asked hopefully.

We usually always did **fun stuff** on Sundays, whether it was going out somewhere cool or staying in to watch a movie and eating vats of popcorn.

The Sunday before Christmas we'd gone to the Festive Fun Fair at the park and I went on the dodgems three times, which was **ace** till I felt like I'd got whiplash.

"How about a board game?" Dad suggested.

"Ooh, yes!" said Fiona, enthusiastically. "That would be nice!"

Parents are big on board games. This is because they played them a lot when they were kids, along with climbing trees and making models out of taped-together toilet roll tubes. That makes board games old-fashioned, and grown-ups think anything that is old-fashioned is very good.

"So, fancy beating your old dad at Monopoly, Indie?" Dad smiled at me.

"Well, I dunno…" I said with a shrug. I mean, I quite like playing board games, but it was a bit of a let-down after mega dodgem denting.

"Ah, but what if it's Monopoly with a twist!" said Dad, with a *mad* glint in his eye.

Dylan immediately glanced up from his DS Lite. Yep, we were both instantly intrigued.

Fiona looked instantly worried and muttered something about checking on how her white choc chip mango muffins were coming along. (She's nearly as allergic to silliness as she is to messiness.)

"Dylan! Go and dig out the Monopoly from your room!" Dad ordered my stepbrother. "Indie – clear the table!"

"And what are you going to do?" I asked Dad, as he strode off after Dylan.

"Aha!!" he said – with a manic grin – over his shoulder.

For a second or two, I concentrated on tidying the table (i.e. taking Dad's photography magazines off it and shoving them under the sofa.)

But I could hear a lot of rumbling and banging coming from somewhere in the hall. So I peeked; the door to the cupboard under the stairs was open.

"Huff! Uh!! Hunufff!!" I heard Dad grumble breathlessly, as if he was wrestling with some under-the-stairs Hoover monster or something.

OOPS – he was now backing his way out, which meant it was time for me to retreat fast, leap silently onto the sofa and pretend I hadn't been trying to spy.

"Ready?!" said Dad two seconds later, as he appeared in the doorway with the entire contents of the coat rack.

"Ready for what?' I asked, noticing Dylan following him in with the Monopoly box in his hand.

"Ready to play an old game, but with daft rules?!" Dad announced, all perky.

"Are we playing it outside?" Dylan asked dubiously, staring at the coat mountain and then at the drizzle outside the window.

"Nope," laughed Dad, dropping the coat mountain on the floor (ooh, Fiona wouldn't like that). "In the normal rules, every time you get a six on the dice, what happens?"

"You get an extra turn?" Dylan blinked at my dad.

"Yes – in the new daft rules, you also have to put on a coat when you roll a six!" Dad announced.

Dylan's eyes lit up, probably because his very smart brain works in a slightly daft way anyway. As for me, living with three daft dogs has probably rubbed off on me.

"**Yay!**" I said, rushing to
set up the board.

It was the most fun
game of Monopoly ever.

By the time Fiona came back in the room carrying a tray of something that smelled very good, I could hardly move (I was wearing five coats, including Dad's parka), never mind reach out for a warm muffin.

Two hours later, we'd done Snakes and Ladders (putting socks on our hands every time we rolled a six – just try picking up a dice with seven of those on each hand), and played a game of Frustration putting (clean) pants on our heads every time a six cropped up.

I swear Fiona hid in the kitchen the whole time, to avoid the daftness and clothing-related messiness.

MORE WAYS TO HAVE OLD-FASHIONED FUN FOR FREE

Toast draughts

Invented by Dad one Sunday when I was round at his place. Me and Dylan had been just about to play normal draughts, when Dylan remembered he'd taken his set into school on the last day of term.

Somehow three white draughts and four black ones had gone missing, and an unknown person managed to spill red paint across the board.

Fiona was a bit cross at first (she reminded Dylan about the time he took his Lego fire station into school when he was five and ended up coming home crying, with only three Lego bricks and a window).

But then Dad interrupted with an amazing, edible piece of inspiration.

First, he asked a slightly confused Fiona if she could stick some toast on.

Then, he drew out a lookalike draughtboard on a plain piece of paper.

Next, he shouted through to Fiona, asking her to spread one piece of toast with jam, and one with peanut butter.

She was cool with that, but confused again when he asked her to cut out ten pence-sized circles in the toast.

She saw (and we saw) what was going on once he set up our game for us.

The rules were easy-peasy:
they were the same as
normal draughts,
except if you won
a piece, you ate it!
(MMMM...)

Upside-down jigsaw puzzle

Caitlin's idea; we did it together on the kitchen table on Tuesday afternoon. It's much trickier and **madder** than doing it the right way up.

Warning: jigsaws are best played with no crutches. (I nudged one of Caitlin's and it knocked the box full of pieces all over the floor. We still haven't found the very top of Cinderella's fairytale castle. It's either under the fridge or Dibbles ate it.)

Rude hopscotch

Instead of numbers, draw silly faces in chalk on paving stones. Every time you land on one, make a matching stupid sound to go with it, like blowing a raspberry. (Stop when little old lady neighbours are passing, or they'll think you've got horrible manners, instead of just a strange imagination.)

"I Spy" something difficult

"I spy with my little eye, something beginning with…"; hey, that's too easy! Make it "I spy with my little eye, something ENDING with…" just to make it harder, and show who's got the sparkiest braincells!

(Answer: not me. I've played this game six times now with Caitlin and she always wins. Well, apart from the time she tried to LET me win, by saying "T" and staring very hard our ca"T". I still said "Huh? Smudge?" and lost.)

Scissors, paper, slime

Just like 'Scissors, paper, stone', only with, er, slime (very good fun to mime). The only changes to the rules are: scissors slip off slime (slime wins) and paper squashes slime (paper wins, though it goes a bit crinkly).

Doing slime and slime at the same time means your fingers get in a tangle.

Fun in the sun!

(Or outside, at least...)

I was four, and my big cousins Emma and Claire were huge.

OK, they must have been nine and ten at the time, but they seemed like practically grown-ups to me. I think I probably expected them to drive cars and know how stuff like electricity and tax worked.

The trouble was, I didn't see Emma and Claire very often (they lived three hours' drive away).

So whenever they came to visit, I'd spend the first few hours all tongue-tied and shy – and then decide they were **fantastic** in the last ten minutes before they left.

It was the same this particular Saturday.

While Mum was chatting with her sister (Auntie Suzanne) and Auntie Suzanne's husband (Uncle Barry), I had been shooed out into the sunny garden with Emma and Claire.

"So, are you at school yet?" Emma (the one who was nine) asked me.

"Mmmnmm," I mumbled in a teeny-tiny voice.

Emma looked at Claire (the one who was ten) to see if she understood what I'd squeaked. Claire just frowned to show she didn't.

"Who's your best friend, then, Indie?" Emma tried again.

"Mnnnummmff munnuffinum," I mumbled some more.

"Uh… what games do you like to play?" asked Claire, taking a turn.

I shrugged.

Emma and Claire looked at each other, probably wishing they were back home instead of being here with a small mute person.

A small mute person who looked terrified of them.

Then Emma smiled at Claire, leant over and whispered in her ear. Claire broke into an instant beaming smile.

I thought Emma had probably suggested they go ask my mum if it was alright to ignore me for the afternoon, because I was so dull.

"You stay there, Indie!" they told me, as they grinned and scuttled towards the house. "We've got to ask Auntie Lynne something…"

Yikes – Auntie Lynne was my mum! I was right! They were going to check if it was OK to ignore me!!

I spent an anxious few minutes staying completely still, doing exactly as I was told, even though I'd started to need the loo.

"Right!" said Emma and Claire at the same time, as they bundled back out into the garden together.

Mum, Auntie Suzanne and Uncle Barry followed them, smiling.

I couldn't figure out what that meant.

And I couldn't figure out why my cousins were carrying a very random bunch of stuff from my house.

"We're going to have a sports day!!" announced Emma, pulling flippers on over her shoes. "A stupid one!"

"Dad's going to time us!" said Claire, handing me one end of the skipping rope.

I held it, not sure why.

"You and Claire go to the far side of the garden, and hold the skipping rope up high as a finishing line," Mum explained.

She'd spotted that I was a bit confused (and worried).

"You're all going to take turns doing the different events," Auntie Suzanne joined in, "and Uncle Barry will time you. I'll be keeping score on the chalkboard!"

Because I was busy watching her scribble our names, I didn't spot the fact that Mum had blown up my old rubber ring and slipped it over Emma's head and arms.

"Ready, Em?"
Uncle Barry laughed.

"Ready!" said my
cousin Emma, taking
her place at the starting
line (a garden cane laid
on the ground).

Emma was poised to take
off, in her very special outfit.

"Twice around the garden and then
straight to the finishing line!" Uncle Barry
ordered her. "GO!!"

Emma did it in 20.5 seconds.

Claire was faster, with 18 seconds.

I did it in 34.4 seconds, which everyone
said was very good, considering my feet
were so small they kept slipping out of the
flippers and I had to keep stopping to put
them back on again.

We played four more games:

1) The Soup-Ladle-and-Melon Race: our version of an egg-and spoon race. (We didn't have any eggs and the only round thing Mum could suggest was a melon, which wouldn't have fitted on a spoon.)

2) The Tea-Tray-and-Marbles Race: balancing a whole bunch of marbles on a tray as you run around a garden is very tricky. And noisy too.

3) The Half-Filled-Hot-Water-Bottle-Balanced-On-The-Head Race: mainly because we didn't have a beanbag to use.

4) Pillowcase Race: like the sack race, only you put it over your head instead of stepping into it and hopping. You have to make your way around the course (i.e. garden) with someone guiding you round by telling you to go left, right or straight ahead. (Beware: you MUST know your lefts and rights to do this game. I didn't, and accidentally made Claire run into the clothes pole.)

In the end, Emma had scored three points (for coming first in the last three races).

Claire scored two points (one for coming first in the Running-In-Flippers race, and one to make up for running into the clothes pole).

I scored one hundred and fifty points (I think Auntie Suzanne might have fiddled the scores slightly to let me win).

"**ooooh!**" I squealed, as they all gave me a round of applause, and Mum presented me with the melon as a prize.

But I wasn't squealing because I was pleased. It was because I'd suddenly realized something I should have done at the beginning of our wacky races.

And that was the fastest time I did that day: the two-second dash to the loo…

MORE WAYS TO HAVE FUN IN THE SUN FOR FREE

Obstacle race

The next time Emma and Claire visited, we turned our Silly Sports Day into an Obstacle Race. **Brilliant!**

Cloudspotting

Caitlin and me thought
of this when I helped her hobble
out to the garden for some fresh air.
Basically, you lie back and try to spot
shapes and faces in the clouds. (I thought
one lumpy cloud looked like Dibbles.
Caitlin said it was exacly like Captain Jack
Sparrow, but I couldn't see it myself.)

The no-treasure treasure hunt

Make up a bunch of clues and hide them round the garden for your friends to find. The prize doesn't have to be anything fancy; just a funny drawing or a cheeky poem or something.

When I played it with Dad and Fiona and Dylan, the prize was a slice of banana cake wrapped in tin foil.

Or it would have been, only we played it in the park, and just as Dylan and me found the last clue ('The flowers don't taste as good as the fruit!') and rushed to the cherry blossom tree, we saw a small kid waddling off, stuffing his face with the cake he'd 'luckily' just found...

113

Bury a time capsule

Get a plastic tub and make yourself a time capsule! Mine has a photo of me and Dibbles, a packet of my current favourite sweets – Maltesers – and a letter to myself, explaining what I want to be doing in five years (hanging out with dogs, eating Maltesers, making another time capsule).

Stick it in the garden somewhere, or in a bit of the local park where the gardeners or random dogs aren't likely to dig it up.

Leave it for however long you decide (should be years, not just next time you fancy some Maltesers).

The staring game

A really simple, pointless-but-fun way to pass the time on bus journeys.

Here are the rules:

1. Sit upstairs.
2. Stare down at people passing by.

Um, that's it. But it's kind of spooky how many people realise they're being stared at and look up at you.

How does that work?!?

Whenever someone does look up at you, you have to make sure you give them a little smile or a wave. They'll probably be confused, but secretly pleased.

Arty- crafty fun

(Me and Caitlin go creative crazy)

Last Tuesday night, I dreamt that both Soph and Fee moved away, and took Dibbles and my goldfish with them.

(Why they would take Dibbles and the goldfish makes no sense. But then dreams have a habit of not making sense. A bit like Dylan, really.)

Mum woke up and came through when she heard me shouting, "No! Not the goldfish!!" over and over again.

I can't remember that.

All I can remember is waking up to Mum's cool hand on my forehead and Dibbles' smelly wet tongue licking my toes.

"What you need is a dreamcatcher," Caitlin said at breakfast on Wednesday morning.

By the way, Caitlin hadn't been woken up by my nightmare. She likes to play loud, shouty rock music to relax, so a ten-year-old girl yelping a bit wouldn't have disturbed her sleep at all.

"What's a dreamcatcher?" I asked her.

I was slightly worried. It sounded like the Childcatcher from the film 'Chitty Chitty Bang Bang', and he gave me nightmares for a whole month after I watched it.

"They're these things you hang in your room. They're meant to let nice dreams through and catch the bad dreams."

"What do they look like?" I asked her.

"Hold on – I tore out a magazine article about them once. I'll go look for it…"

Caitlin hobbled off on her crutches. From her room came lots of banging and thudding and rustling for quite a long time.

It sounded like she might be building a tree house in there, not just looking for a few torn pages from a magazine.

After ten more minutes of **banging, thudding, rustling** – plus a bunch of sighing too – Caitlin hobbled back, reading from something clutched in her hand.

"'Dreamcatchers were made by the Ojibwe Native American tribe, and were hung above children's beds to protect them from nightmares.'"

I gazed at the photo on the page.

So a dreamcatcher was a wooden hoop thingymee with spiderweb-y stringy bits in the middle and feathers and beads dangling from it.

It looked nice. Nothing like the Childcatcher.

"Let's make you one!" said Caitlin, enthusiastically, tapping a finger on the page.

"**Yay!**" I answered, excited about making something and excited about having another something to write about in my project.

It sounded so easy to do:

1) cut a thin, bendy branch from a bush in the garden

2) get some string

3) find some beads

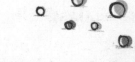

4) find some feathers

But it turned out to be a bit more complicated.

For a start, when I went out in the garden, I tried to bend (and broke) quite a lot of branches before I found one that seemed like it wouldn't mind being curved into a circle shape.

121

I snipped it off the bush, stuck it on the ground for a second while I put Mum's gardening scissors away, and then came back to find my perfect branch being chewed into twiglets by Dibbles.

Another branch later, and I was back in the kitchen. When I'd left Caitlin, she was going to raid her jewellery box for beads she didn't need, and then raid the kitchen drawers in search of string.

But when I caught sight of her, she was lying flat on the floor, as if she'd collapsed.

"What's wrong?" I said in a panic, falling down on my knees beside her.

"Smudge woke up," mumbled Caitlin.

Now this was strange, for a couple of reasons.

Reason a: Smudge doesn't wake up very often (she's a fat cat snoozing machine)

Reason b: I didn't see how Smudge waking up could have made Caitlin collapse. Had she attacked her? Dug her claws into Caitlin's injured liga-thingy?

Then I noticed that Caitlin was waggling a wooden spoon under the fridge, while an intrigued Smudge sat watching her.

"What did she do?" I asked, sensing now that Caitlin hadn't been attacked by our elderly moggy, but still not sure what had actually happened.

123

"I found some beads and put them on the table," said Caitlin, wobbling the wooden spoon back and forth. "But when I went to look for string, Smudge had spotted them and started batting them around with her paw. They landed on the floor and she started skittering after them when I was trying to pick them up."

With a deft **flick** of the spoon, Caitlin suddenly batted a handful of (dusty) beads out – and I scrabbled around and rescued them all before Smudge could pounce on them again.

But actually, she'd now padded off and started playing with the string that Caitlin had left dangling from the kitchen drawer.

"Nope!" I said, trying to grab the string while Smudge firmly held onto it with her claws. But I quickly fixed that.

So at last we had everything we needed to begin. Here's how we did it:

Step 1) Caitlin closed the kitchen door to prevent pet interference.

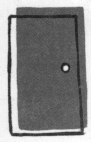

Step 2) I gently bent the branch around, and Caitlin tried a piece of string tightly round the two ends to keep them together.

Step 3) I stretched the string over to one side of the branch hoop, and looped it round.

126

Step 4) I did step 3 a lot more times, till it looked like a spider web.

Step 5) Caitlin threaded beads on the end of three bits of string, and tied them onto the bottom of the dreamcatcher.

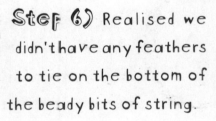

Step 6) Realised we didn't have any feathers to tie on the bottom of the beady bits of string.

Step 7) Nearly decided not to bother with feathers, and then worried that the spirits of the Ojibwe Native Americans might be fed up with us for not trying hard enough.

127

Step 8) Went over to see Mrs O'Neill.

Step 9) Tied a tiny yellow budgie feather to the bottom of each of the beady bits, thanks to Mrs O'Neill checking the bottom of Archie's cage.

And on Wednesday night, I'm pleased to report that I had no nightmares.

Only a very odd dream about having a pet spider called Ojibwe...

MORE WAYS TO HAVE ARTY-CRAFTY FUN FOR FREE

Good luck voodoo doll

When Caitlin suggested making voodoo dolls, it made me feel a bit icky. I'd heard of people making little puppety dolls of people they didn't like and doing mean stuff like sticking pins in them.

"But you can make good luck voodoo dolls too!" Caitlin insisted.

I don't know if that's an absolutely true thing that everyone knows, or if Caitlin made it up, but we had fun making one for sure.

I thought about who might need some good luck, then I remembered that Soph had an Irish dancing competition in two weeks' time, and might appreciate a little help from me, and an old Pippa doll I found.

The doll didn't look much like Soph, but I sort of tied up her hair a bit like how Soph does hers, made a little Irish dance costume out of a sheet of kitchen roll and felt pens, and – the best bit – made a tiny winners' cup out of tin foil and sellotaped it in her hand.

I sat the Pippa/Soph doll on the shelf, with a bunch of flowers beside her, picked from the garden and stuck in a tumbler. It still didn't look quite magical and lucky enough yet, so we draped her with sparkly old beaded necklaces I used to use for dressing up games when I was little.

When I told Soph yesterday that I made her a good luck voodoo doll, she seemed very choked up. I think she was just extremely touched. Or maybe a little freaked out…

131

Starry, starry ceiling

Cut out cardboard star shapes. Cover them with tin foil. Blu-tack them to your ceiling. Put on just your bedside light, lie down on your bed, gaze at yours stars, and listen to dreamy music. (Or Caitlin parping Christina Aguilera's 'Beautiful' on her didgeridoo, if you're me.)

Make a beanie hat

Caitlin laid out an old stripy jumper of hers on the table. She loved it, but it had a huge raggedy hole in the armpit.

"Meet your new beanie hat!" she told me, which confused me a bit.

Next, I had a tape measure going half-way around my head.

"Thirty-five centimetres," she mumbled, then measured out forty centimetres along the bottom hem of the jumper, marking it with black felt pen. "You've got to leave sewing room."

Do you? I thought, deciding to stay quiet (and puzzled) and just watch.

And what I was watching was Caitlin drawing a semi-circle and cutting out both the back and front of the jumper together.

"Just flip these two halves over onto the wrong side, and stitch them together," ordered Caitlin, passing me the sewing box stuffed full of needles and thread.

So I flipped, and sewed (not very well, but you couldn't see that when I flipped it round the right way again).

And so that was my stripy beanie hat!

(It just a pity that it sort of makes me look like a bee...)

Toilet paper bunting:

You will need string (or long lengths of ribbon, to be fancy), and loo roll and a stapler.

Tear off heaps of sheets of loo roll. Fold each sheet diagonally, to make a triangle. Slip the triangle over the string and staple (or glue) the two sides of the triangle together. Do it loads and loads of times, till you have your bunting.

Warning: this is just a fun thing to hang up in your room and make it look party-ish. Do NOT use it outside. (If it rains, you will just have tiny piles of soggy toilet paper glooped on your path. **Yewwww**.)

Dylan's version of fun

(Yes, it's nuts)

Hello.

My name is Dylan and I am India Kidd's step-brother.

My granny and grandad live in a nice place with a name that I can't say out loud because it always makes me snigger. (It is Shrewsbury in Shropshire – try it.

It's like trying to speak while you're eating five very chewy toffees at once with fake teeth.)

Anyway when I was there during this school holiday visiting my granny and grandad I got a text from Indie saying she was doing a project on how to have fun and did I want to write a bit for it.

I said oh yes please and then she said can you try not to make it too weird and I said I'll try and then she said and please can you try to use commas this time because usually you don't and it makes it very hard for people to read.

After that I thought and I thought and I thought till I got a headache and Granny stared at me strangely and asked if I needed a lie-down or a third slice of jam roly-poly for energy because I was looking a bit peaky.

At the end of our visit to Shrewsbury in Shropshire (ha ha) I got home and switched on the computer and wrote down all the ideas that had been whirling round my head and dumped all the ones that were too weird (like learning to speak pigeon – Mum said all the cooing I was doing was annoying and could I stop it please when she was trying to watch the news) and then I got down to my three best ideas which are all coming up.

(By the way I didn't manage to do so well with commas because they just confuse me and I don't know where to put them in so here are some ,,,,,,,,,,,,, so anybody who is reading this could maybe just look at them and imagine where they should go and then that will be OK for everyone and no-one will find it hard to read thank you.)

Right here are my ideas...

1) Practise saying 'Shrewsbury in Shropshire' ten times in a row really quickly and see how stupid it comes out.

Ha ha ha that is not really one of my ideas. It's only a joke but obviously not to my granny and grandad and other people who live there sorry I'll start again.

Here are my ideas (for real I promise and no more joking around 'cause Indie might not like it and not ask me to do stuff for her projects again)...

1) Do a family tree.

Doing a normal family tree would be very fascinating. Like you start with yourself and then go back to your mum and dad and then to your grandparents who maybe live in Shrewsbury in Shropshire (ha ha sorry) or wherever but then I think maybe there is a more interesting way to do a family tree. Like

   a)make it up. I did one where I started off with me then invented a great-grandad who was a viking and a great-great-great-great-great aunt who was a vampire witch. I got my family tree to go all the way back to the Neolithic period (I missed out a few generations) and wrote that my great-great-grandparents x a milion were a caveman and a fish.

b) make it up for a pet. It is a shame for animals because except for posh fast racing horses who had relatives who were posh fast racing horses no-one knows anything about who their cat was related to in the Middle Ages or anything. So one day I decided that it would be cool to invent a family tree for Indie's dog Dibbles. My favourite bits were that one of his relatives was a lap-dog in the court of Queen Marie Antoinette of France and also that his great-great-granddog was spy in World War II and got parachuted behind enemy lines with vital supplies of dog food for four-legged prisoners of war.

2) Stone pets.

When I was a really little kid I badly wanted a pet but Mum said no you are allergic and you might pat something and then swell up to twice your size and die.

Then one day we went to a beach somewhere where I got really bad sunburn because I rubbed all my suncream off with a towel when my mum wasn't looking because I thought it smelled like marzipan but that doesn't matter right now and Indie will tell me off for waffling.

Anyway while the sun was quietly burning me only I didn't find that out till later when I went a strange shade of tomato I found a smooth round stone that looked a bit like an owl.

I took it home and painted an owl face on it and feathers and stuff. (It cheered me up while half my skin seemed to be peeling off and making me look like a mutant lizard-boy.)

It was so excellent that for ages after that I kept collecting round stones and painting them to be pretend pets until I had an owl a ferret a chinchilla a toad a piglet a heffalump and more.

You know something? I don't know what happened to my pretend pets but one day when I was six-and-three-quarters-and-a-bit I suddenly noticed that I didn't have them anymore.

I asked Mum if she had seen them and she said no but she wouldn't look me in the eye and starting quickly tidying something that didn't need tidying.

Even though I was only six-and-three-quarters-and-a-bit I was pretty sure that it was one of those times that parents are fibbing and have quietly chucked out stuff that they've noticed you haven't played with for ages like giant mega rockets made out of fabric conditioner bottles and a whole roll of tinfoil or thirty-four sheets of paper with identical looking felt pen doodles on them.

Anyway about a month ago me and Indie and Soph and Fee were talking about silly stuff we did when we were little and I told them (Indie Soph and Fee I mean) about them (my stone pets and not the giant mega rocket and felt-pen doodles) and they (Indie Soph and Fee) thought they (the stone pets) sounded very cute actually.

Then Indie said for a laugh why didn't we have a mini-competition and all make up imaginary animals and paint them on some stones and vote for the best one.

Indie painted a frogodile
(green with pointy teeth).

Soph did a parrocat
(fluffy with a beak).

Fee did an elefish
(trunk and scales).

Mine got voted
the best.

It was a hedgedog
(spikes and panting
tongue).

I think I won because I sellotaped
a piece of string to it for a lead and
dragged it round the park.

It was brilliant till George who is Indie's greyhound started growling at it then ran off with it and buried it somewhere in the ornamental rose bushes.

(Indie says he's done that with a frisbee one Croc shoe a set of keys and a copy of 'Animals & You' lately.)

3) Toss an M&M in the air and catch it in your mouth.

It is very impressive and cool when you see people chucking M&Ms in the air or peanuts or something and then catching them in their mouths.

I saw Abdul Samed in my class do it a couple of weeks ago and everyone went "whoaaah!". I thought it must be good to have people go "whoaaah!" at you in an impressed sort of way so a day or so later I snuck a bag of yogurt-covered raisins in my room so I could teach myself to do it too.

I practised and practised chucking and catching for two hours when I was suppcsed to be tidying my collections which are dinosaurs (books and models and stuff) and Star Wars (sticker books and figures and stuff) and conkers (367).

Teaching yourself to chuck and catch stuff in your mouth is best to do in your own room with no one watching. That's 'cause there's no-one around to groan every time a yogurt-covered raisin or whatever goes on the floor or say 'Yuck!' when you pick it up off the carpet and blow the fluff off and eat it anyway.

(By the way I didn't manage to catch any in my mouth that time only in my eye which made it sting a bit. But I am going to try again tonight with a bag of Hula Hoops though they are salt and vinegar so I think I need to do it with my sunglasses on.)

OK so those were my ideas and I hope you like them a lot. Or maybe even just a little bit.

(After I e-mailed this to Indie she e-mailed me back to say that maybe for fun I should learn about commas. I thought very hard about that but then realised that commas make me think of little random mouse poos dotted between words and I decided I wouldn't bother.)

Why I'm banning the word 'boring'

(Oh, and some fun stuff that went wrong...)

When Mum was admiring the bunting I'd strung up (OK, after it fell off on her head and I had untangled her), I asked what **fun-for-free** stuff she'd done when she was my age.

She looked thoughtful for a second, then winced.

"What?" I asked.

"Oh, nothing," she said, all flustered.

"What sort of nothing?" I asked again.

All that flustering seemed too interesting to ignore.

Mum rolled her eyes, blushed, and started to tell me what she'd got up to, and why it had got her flustered.

Here's the thing: when she was seven, she was madly into

> **a)** animals (no change there, then) and...
>
> **b)** fashion (she was mad on this for a long time — she used to be a model, though you'd never think it now, looking at the khaki work clothes she lives in and the hamster bedding that's always sticking out of her hair)

Anyway, back when she was seven, she combined her two favourite things.

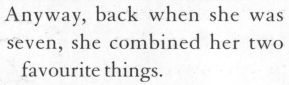

Draping a sparkly scarf around her cat Dizzy's neck was probably OK, I suppose.

But painting Dizzy's claws with peach nail varnish wasn't such a good idea.

Her mum (my nana) caught her just as Dizzy was about to lick it off and probably poison herself.

Nana got well scratched as she tried to hold Dizzy long enough to apply nail varnish remover and wash the whole chemical mess off, while Mum hid in her room and made Dizzy a 'Sorry I tried to poison you and nearly made you ill' card with glitter and sparkly stickers.

155

Actually, Dad pulled the same kind of "Oops, I wish I hadn't just remembered that!" face when I asked him the same question.

It turned out that when he was a kid, he was mad about an American stuntman called Evel Knievel.

He tried to reenact one of Mr Knievel's stunts by building a ramp for his pushbike and laying out a bunch of his toy cars to leap over.

His parents thought that was pretty cute.

They didn't find it so **cute** when he trotted back into the kitchen and asked for some matches. Turned out he'd built a small bonfire of old wood next to the ramp and was all hyped up for his next jump stunt, i.e. setting himself on fire.

But while poisoning your beloved pet or ending up in casualty is not an ideal way to have fun, everything I've written about in my project this week has made me realise that there's never any reason to be bored.

You don't need lots of money or things to have a good time. All you need is (a slightly weird) imagination.

In fact, the words 'boring' and 'bored' should be banned.

boring ~~ ~~

bored ~~ ~~

If anyone ever finds themselves about to say these words, Caitlin and me have come up with something to say instead:

"Be-doing."

I mean, if you're fed-up, but say, "I feel a bit be-doing", it's going to make you feel silly and smiley straight away, and more in the mood to think of fun things to do.

So that is it: my fun-for-free project.

I hope you liked it, and didn't find it too **Be-doing-y**...

xxxxxxxxxxxxxxxxxxxxxxxxxxxxx